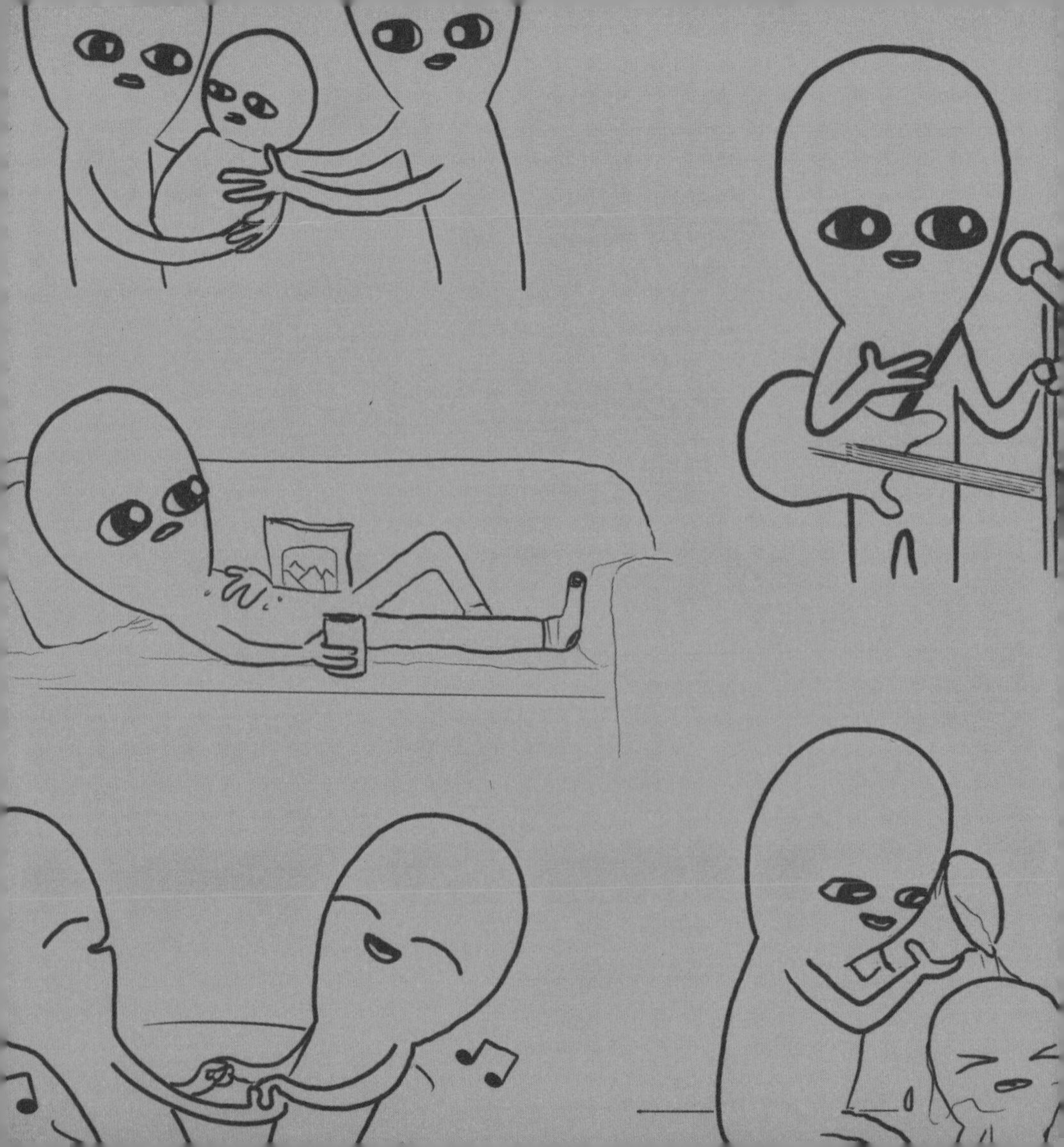

WELCOME BACK TO STRANGE PLANET

THAT WAS THE FINAL MELODY. SINCERELY.

INSINCERE! INSINCERE!

INSINCERE! INSINCERE!

ACTUALLY WE KNOW MORE MELODIES

NATHAN W PYLE

STRANGER PLANET

FIRST PUBLISHED IN THE UNITED STATES IN 2020 BY HARPERCOLLINS BOOKS.

FIRST PUBLISHED IN THE UK IN 2020 BY WILDFIRE, AN IMPRINT OF THE HEADLINE PUBLISHING GROUP.

FIRST EDITION
DESIGNED BY NATHAN W. PYLE
ISBN 978 14722 7585 1

HEADLINE PUBLISHING GROUP, AN HACHETTE UK COMPANY, CARMELITE HOUSE, 50 VICTORIA EMBANKMENT, LONDON
EC4Y 0DZ

WWW.HEADLINE.CO.UK
WWW.HACHETTE.CO.UK

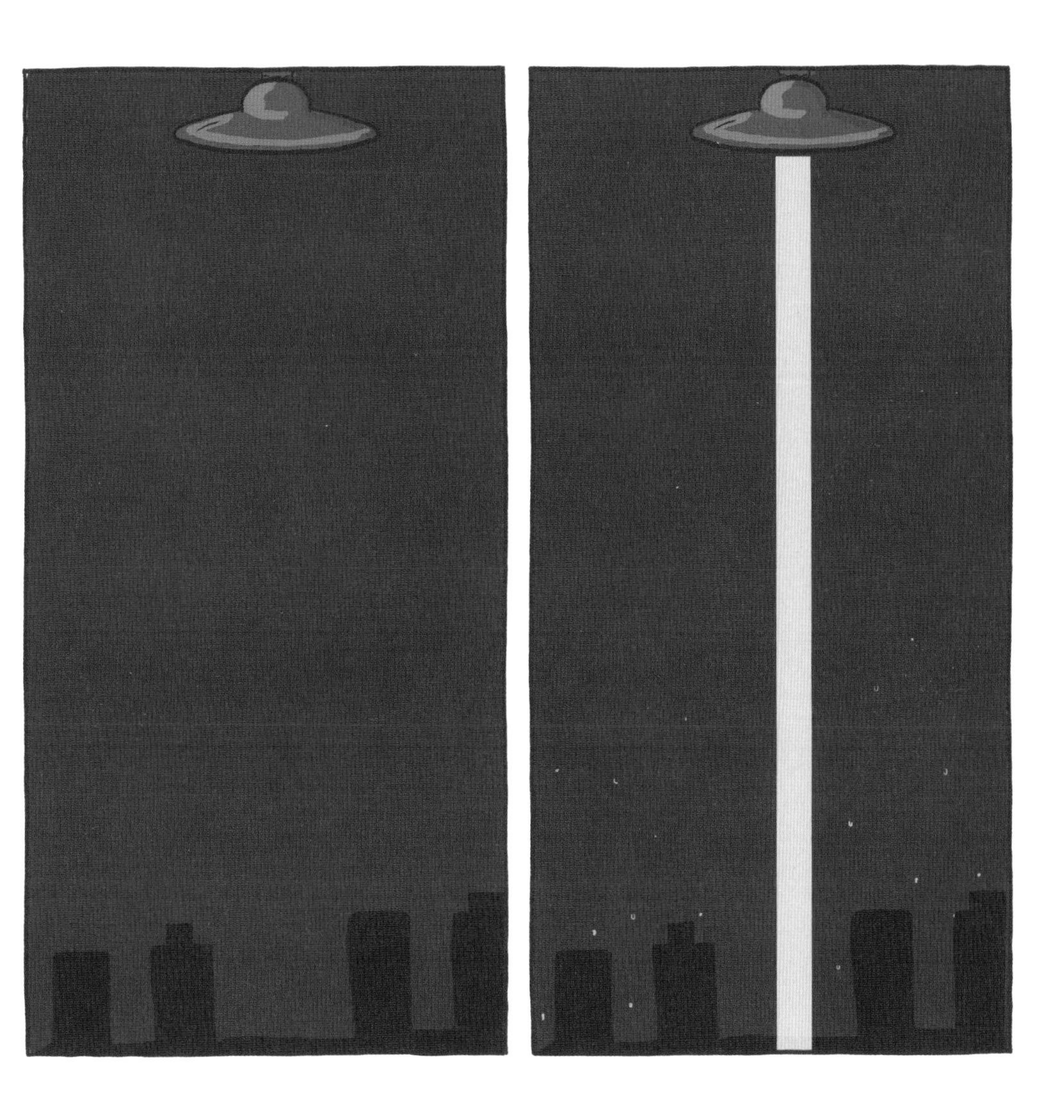

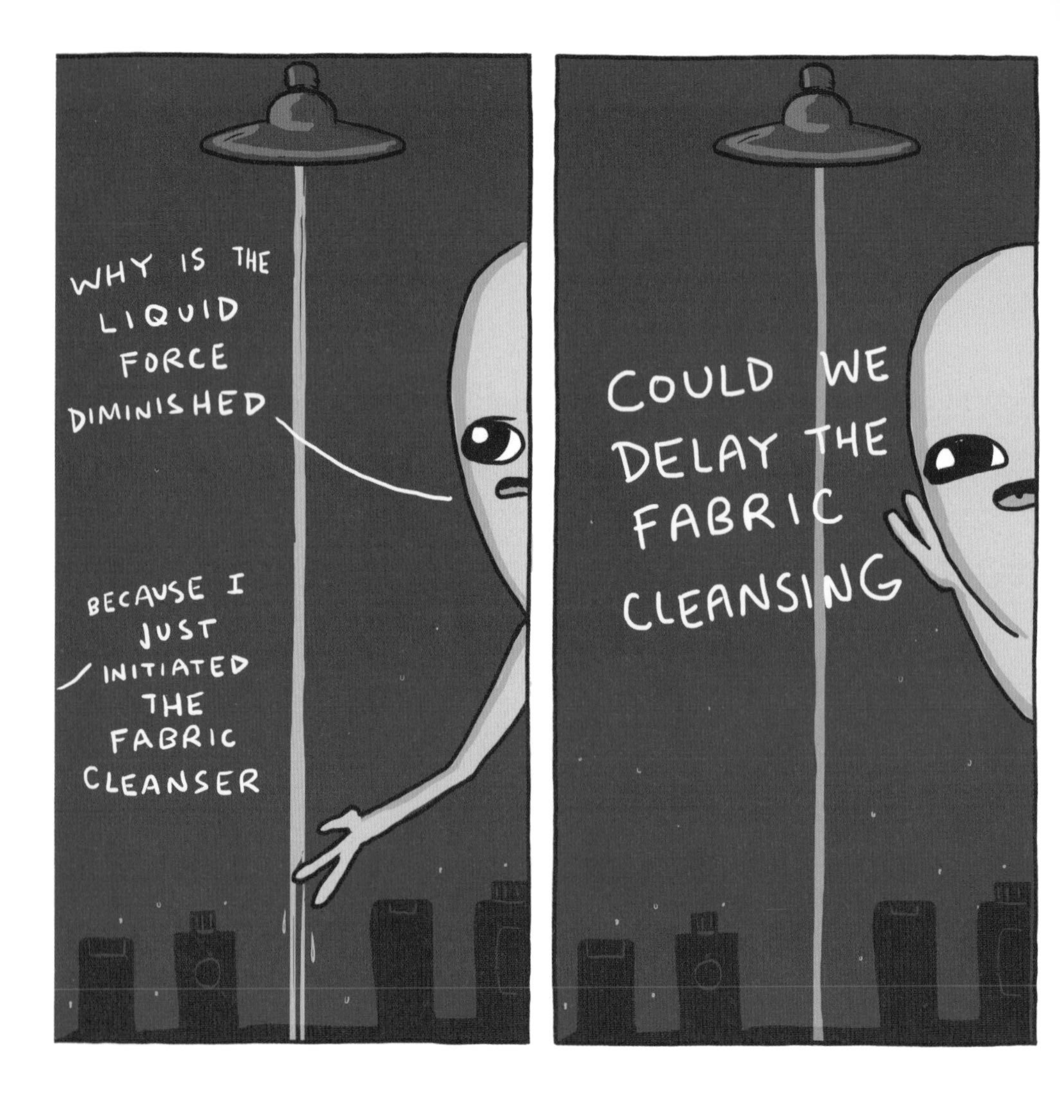
WHY IS THE LIQUID FORCE DIMINISHED
BECAUSE I JUST INITIATED THE FABRIC CLEANSER
COULD WE DELAY THE FABRIC CLEANSING

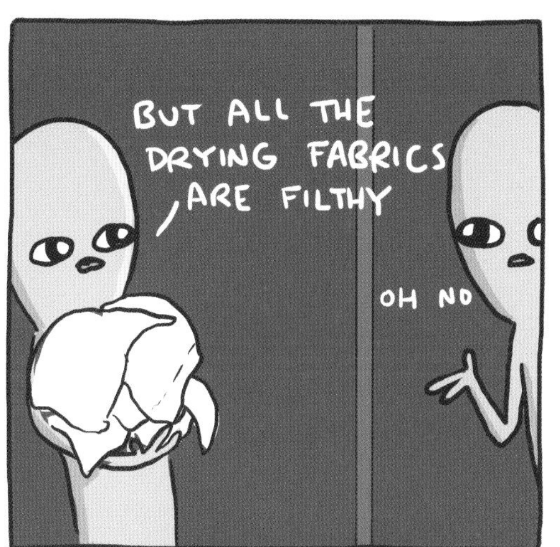
BUT ALL THE DRYING FABRICS ARE FILTHY
OH NO

I WAS HOPING TO BE BOTH CLEAN AND DRY
YOU WILL HAVE TO CHOOSE ONE

HOW ARE THERE NO CLEANSED FABRICS?

BECAUSE WE NEGLECTED TO CLEANSE THEM
AH CONSEQUENCES

TRADITIONS

PROVIDE A SWEET
OR
FACE MILD HARRASSMENT

NOW YOU COMMIT TO COHESION AS LONG AS YOU BOTH SURVIVE
SAY YOU GUARANTEE IT
I GUARANTEE IT
DISPLAY THE DIGIT LOOPS
NICE
OK NOW MOUTHPUSH

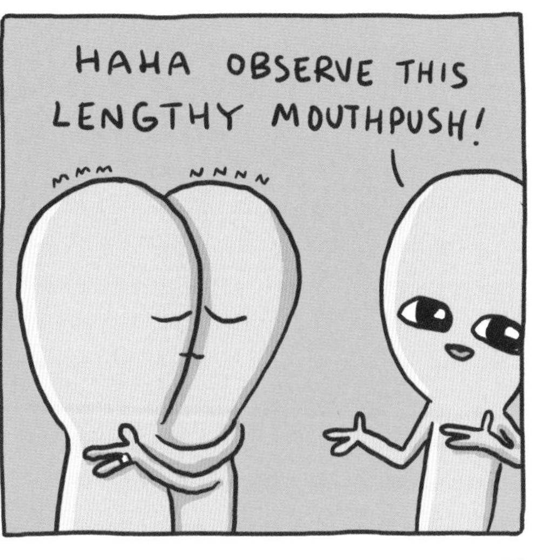
HAHA OBSERVE THIS LENGTHY MOUTHPUSH!
MMM
NNNN

I DECLARE THE COHESION
SUCCESSFUL

CATCH MY DYING PLANTS

MY COHESION IS IMMINENT

WE WANT TO INGEST SOME MILD POISON

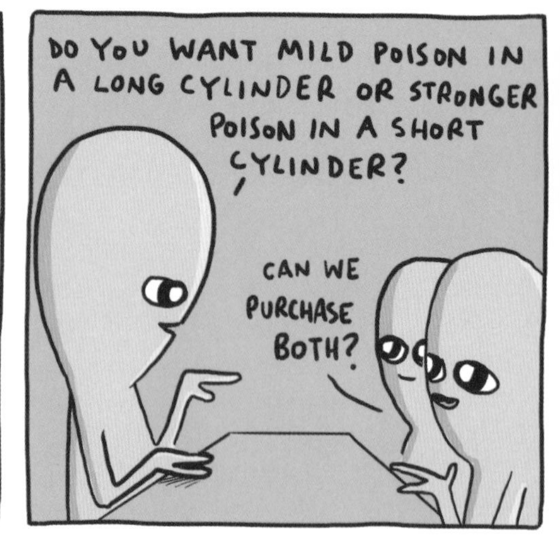
DO YOU WANT MILD POISON IN A LONG CYLINDER OR STRONGER POISON IN A SHORT CYLINDER?
CAN WE PURCHASE BOTH?

YES FOR IT IS JOYFUL HOUR
JOYFUL HOUR
+
COMBINATION
IT IS STILL JOYFUL HOUR?

IT IS JOYFUL HOUR FOR 2 MORE HOURS
JOYFUL HOUR
+
COMBINATION
WONDERFUL

BUT FIRST—HAVE YOU BEEN ON THE PLANET LONG ENOUGH TO INGEST MILD POISON?
JOYFUL HOUR
COMBINATION

IT FEELS GOOD TO BE SUSPECTED OF LAWLESSNESS
OBSERVE

THE IMAGES ARE NOT ATTRACTIVE

THIS IS THE NATURE OF PROVING IMAGES
SO TRUE, BEING

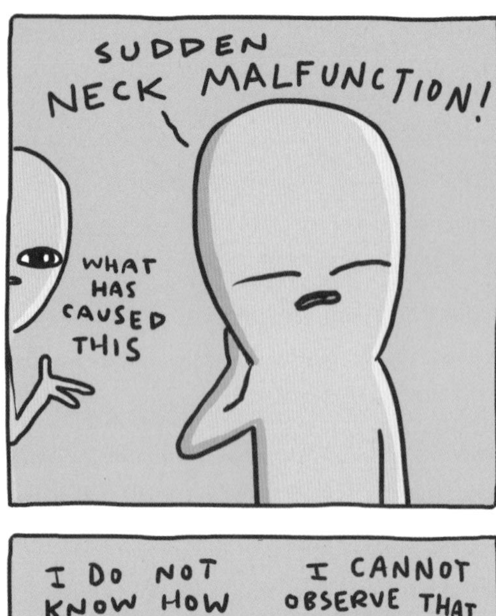
SUDDEN NECK MALFUNCTION!
WHAT HAS CAUSED THIS

I THINK IT WAS MY PROLONGED EXISTENCE

I DO NOT KNOW HOW TO ASSIST YOU
I CANNOT OBSERVE THAT DIRECTION

WELL.. IT'S NOT THAT GREAT
THANK YOU THIS HELPS

I'M READY TO BE HANDPUSHED INTO THE TABLE

LIE DOWN WHILE I MAKE MY HANDS SLIPPERY

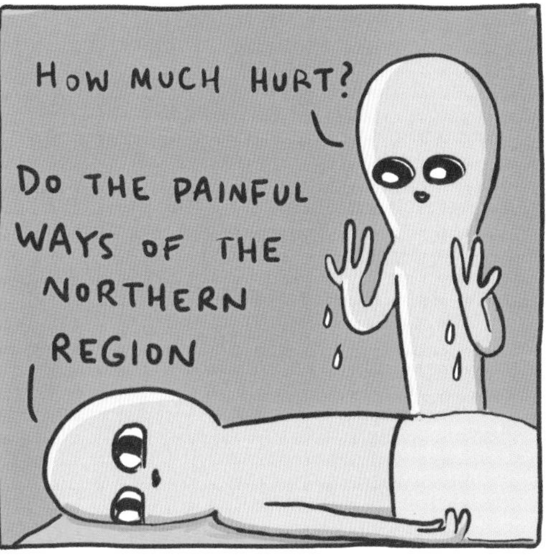
HOW MUCH HURT?
DO THE PAINFUL WAYS OF THE NORTHERN REGION

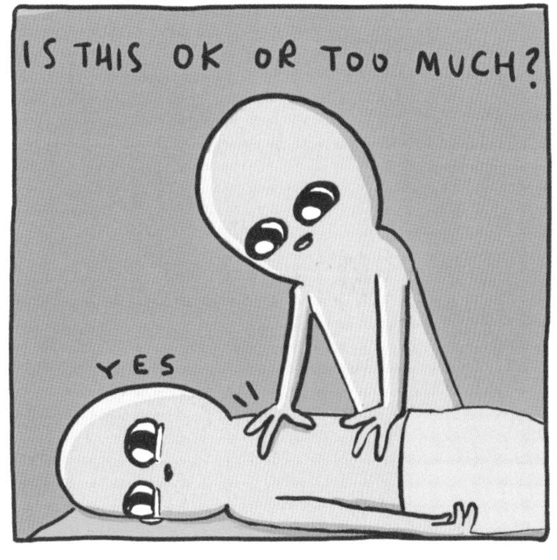
IS THIS OK OR TOO MUCH?
YES

OH MY MORALITY
WE HAVE NOT ENCOUNTERED EACH OTHER IN REVOLUTIONS

TOO MUCH HAS OCCURRED TO DISCUSS
BEST NOT TO EVEN ATTEMPT

YOUR OFFSPRING HAVE LENGTHENED
LIKE AGGRESSIVE PLANTS

I RECALL THEY WERE PREVIOUSLY THIS LONG
I KEPT GIVING THEM SUSTENANCE

YOUR LIFEGIVER AND I TRAVEL BACK A GREAT DISTANCE

WE DO NOT KNOW WHO YOU ARE
OR WHAT THAT PHRASE MEANS

WELL I WANTED TO INCLUDE YOU IN THE CONVERSATION
UNNECESSARY

WHAT A DELIGHTFUL EXCHANGE
SO GLAD WE COLLIDED

THEY DROP BACK TO PROPEL- BUT THEY MERELY RUN INSTEAD! PROGRESS!
CONVINCING DECEPTION!

WAIT - THERE IS A CLOTH!
CLOTH ON THE SEQUENCE! IT MAY BE INVALID

NUMBER 35 USED SUPERFLUOUS VIOLENCE. SHOVING AFTER SHOVE TIME WAS OVER.
THE PROGRESS IS INVALID. THEY WILL REGRESS.

YOU'VE GOT TO REGULATE YOUR SHOVES
WE ALL DO REALLY

MANY TIME INCREMENTS LATER...
THE KICK IS UP!
THE KICK IS ACCURATE!

AND THAT DECIDES THE CONTEST!
OH-WAIT, OBSERVE THIS

THEY'RE DOUSING THEIR SUPERVISOR...
15

THAT IS THE IMPROPER HYDRATION EVERY SUPERVISOR HOPES FOR
IT TRULY IS

WHEN YOU APPROACH A HOME, WHAT IS YOUR ULTIMATUM?

PROVIDE A SWEET!
OR?
FACE MILD HARASSMENT!

THESE BEINGS ARE NOT PARTICIPATING. WE WILL NOT DISTURB THEM
WAIT WHAT

YOU WANT SUCROSE NOT CONFLICT
TODAY
ALL DAYS

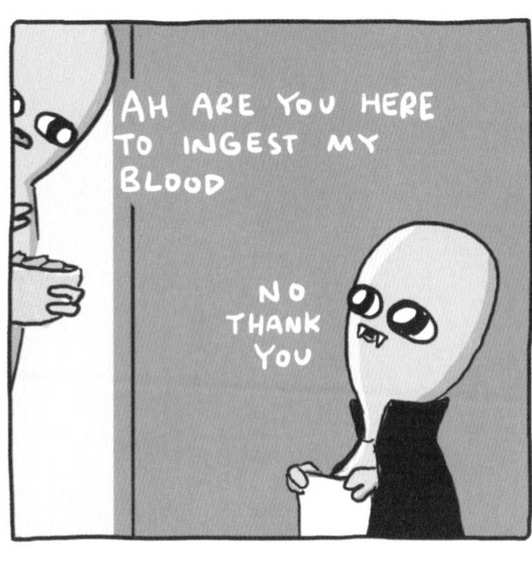
AH ARE YOU HERE TO INGEST MY BLOOD
NO THANK YOU

AH
THE ACCESSORIES ARE A DECEPTION

PROVIDE A SWEET OR FACE MILD HARASSMENT

THEY JUST HAND YOU THE SUCROSE
YES ENJOY YOUR YOUTH

JUST TWO

WAIT CEASE

I HAVE MADE A MISTAKE

WHAT THE UNPLEASANT NONSENSE

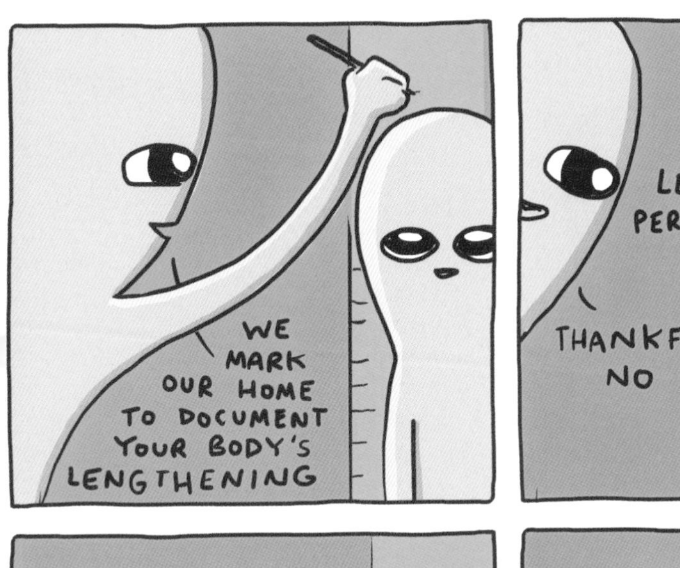
WE MARK OUR HOME TO DOCUMENT YOUR BODY'S LENGTHENING

WILL MY BODY LENGTHEN PERPETUALLY?
THANKFULLY NO

IT WILL CEASE IN THIS APPROXIMATE AREA
WHAT HAPPENS THEN

THEN YOUR BODY IS LONG ENOUGH TO SEARCH FOR YOUR OWN HOME
W H O A

WHETHER IT IS YOUR INSTRUCTOR OR THE BEING WHO PREPARED MY JITTER LIQUID, EACH BEING'S EXISTENCE E X P A N D S FAR BEYOND THEIR VOCATION.

DO YOU UNDERSTAND?

THE REST HOUR IS HERE
BUT I CANNOT LOCATE MY FABRIC PREDATOR CREATURE
AGAIN?

YOU FREQUENTLY MISPLACE IT AT THIS HOUR AND I SENSE THIS IS A DELAYING TECHNIQUE
I AM SEARCHING

DISREGARD! I LOCATED IT
RELIEVED
NOW GO

I DO NOT TRUST OUR TINY OFFSPRING
NOR SHOULD YOU

WE WANT TO BE IN MORTAL DANGER SAFELY
WE HAVE CURRENCY
TORMENTED DWELLING!
WE OBSERVED A SIMILAR STRUCTURE OVER THERE
WE DID NOT ENTER BECAUSE IT APPEARED GENUINELY DANGEROUS
TORMENTED DWELLING!
PROCEED IF YOU POSSESS COURAGE
WE DO NOT
AS WE JUST SAID
ENTED
LLING!
THIS PERISHED BEING INTENDS TO HARM US
HAHA WONDERFUL

WE ARE NOT WELCOME HERE
I AM SO GLAD WE CAME

OBSERVE THE EXIT
I'M SO GLAD WE'RE LEAVING

THANK YOU! PLEASE TELL OTHERS ABOUT THE DISTRESS YOU EXPERIENCED
ORMENTED
WELLING

WE DO EVERY DAY
IT IS A HEALTHY PRACTICE

I HAVE INSTALLED THE FESTIVE ILLUMINATION
TO CELEBRATE THE SPECIAL DAY

AND MANY DAYS AFTER IT
NO NEED TO UNINSTALL

MANY DAYS ARE SPECIAL
AND TINY LIGHTS COULD CELEBRATE MANY THINGS

ANYTHING THAT IS SIGNIFICANT
SUCH AS OUR APATHY
IT IS SIGNIFICANT

SHOULD WE REMOVE THE FILTH UP HERE
IS IT OBSERVABLE
ONLY IF ONE STANDS ON THE FURNISHINGS
OK
THEN WE MUST KEEP VISITORS FROM DOING THIS
THIS SEEMS WISE REGARDLESS

THIS WILL MAKE THE CREATURE APPEAR TO BE A DIFFERENT CREATURE
MILD DECEPTION!

INNOVATION IS OUR SPECIES' GREATEST STRENGTH

THE CREATURE SMILES WITHOUT UNDERSTANDING

UNQUALIFIED JOY IS THE CREATURE'S GREATEST STRENGTH

THE ERRATIC CREATURE IS OBSESSED WITH THE FESTIVE OBJECTS
SHOULD WE SECURE THEM?

THE OBJECTS ARE MEANT TO BE PRECARIOUS AND DELICATE
THIS IS A DILEMMA

I WISH THE OBJECTS BROUGHT THE CREATURE JOY
THEY DO

...IN THEIR POTENTIAL FOR DESTRUCTION
OUR JOYS ARE AT ODDS
YES

I WROTE MY NAME ILLEGIBLY
GREAT

CAN WE TOUCH HANDS
YES

TOO TIGHT?
NO I RESPECT IT

I WILL NOW BOUNCE IT ONCE
FEELS APPROPRIATE

COMPLETION.
THE PERFECT SEQUENCE OF MELODIES

next

next

next

WELCOME TO RECREATIONAL FACE-STRIKING.
WE WILL START BY STRIKING THE HEFTY CYLINDER
WILL WE BE STRIKING FACES TODAY?
ARE YOU PREPARED TO HAVE YOUR FACE STRUCK?
NO
IF YOU ARE NOT READY FOR FACE STRIKES YOU ARE NOT READY TO STRIKE FACES
FAIR

SO DO THE HANDCOVERS HELP PROTECT OUR FACES?
NO

THE HANDCOVERS PROTECT YOUR HANDS SO YOU CAN STRIKE FACES LONGER
WOW
OK

HOW DO WE KNOW WHEN THE CONTEST IS OVER
THAT DEPENDS

BUT IF ONE BEING IS UNCONSCIOUS IT IS OFFICIALLY OVER
I SHOULD HOPE SO

I FORM THE MELODY, SO I WILL POSITION MYSELF IN FRONT

I DEFTLY PLUCK THESE THICK METAL STRANDS, SO I WILL STAND BESIDE YOU

I HAVE SURROUNDED MYSELF WITH OBJECTS I CAN STRIKE SO I WILL STAY SAFELY BACK HERE
THANK YOU
THIS DOES SEEM RIGHT FOR YOU

WE ARE GOING TO BECOME THE NEXT LARGE OBJECT

CERTAIN NIGHTS WE MUST INGEST
SUSTENANCE THAT'S
NOT THE BEST

IT'S NEITHER SAVORY NOR SWEET,
WE MAY HAVE APPLIED EXTRA HEAT

IT DOES NOT HAVE A PLEASANT TASTE
BUT THERE'S TOO MUCH TO GO TO WASTE

WE'LL THINK ABOUT WHAT WE'LL MAKE NEXT-
PERHAPS A CHOICE THAT'S LESS COMPLEX

THE SMALL EIGHT-LEGGED CREATURE ASCENDS THE LIQUID DRAIN

THEN LIQUID FLOWS! ITS GRIP IT CAN'T MAINTAIN!

THE STAR MAKES THE DRAIN DRY AS IT WAS BEFORE

AND THE SMALL EIGHT-LEGGED CREATURE ASCENDS THE DRAIN ONCE MORE

MY CONSCIOUSNESS PERSISTS

HAVE YOU NUMBERED WOOLEN CREATURES
INEFFECTIVE

PLEASE REATTEMPT. I MUST REST FOR TOMORROW'S EVENTS
WHAT OCCURS TOMORROW?

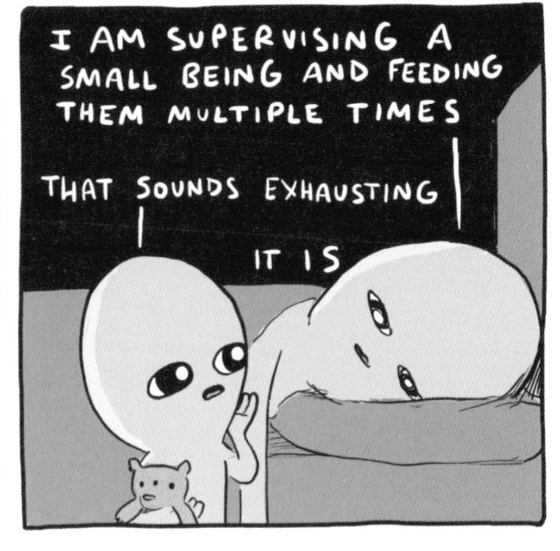
I AM SUPERVISING A SMALL BEING AND FEEDING THEM MULTIPLE TIMES
THAT SOUNDS EXHAUSTING
IT IS

WE WANT PAINFUL SUSTENANCE
HOW MUCH DISCOMFORT CAN YOU PUT US IN

MANY HAVE REGRETTED ORDERING THIS
IDEAL FOR OUR HUBRIS

HOW IS YOUR ANGUISH
UNBEARABLE
WORSE THAN WE'D IMAGINED

YOUR EYES LEAK
YET WE CANNOT TOUCH THEM
A DELIGHTFUL DILEMMA

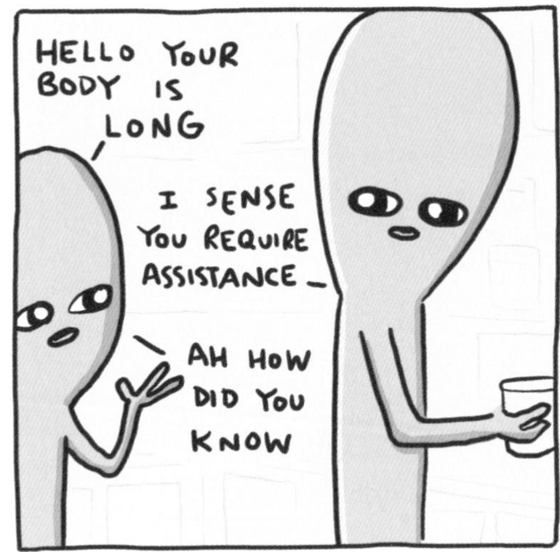
HELLO YOUR BODY IS LONG
I SENSE YOU REQUIRE ASSISTANCE
AH HOW DID YOU KNOW

BECAUSE THIS OCCURS SO FREQUENTLY
APOLOGIES THIS MUST BE TIRESOME

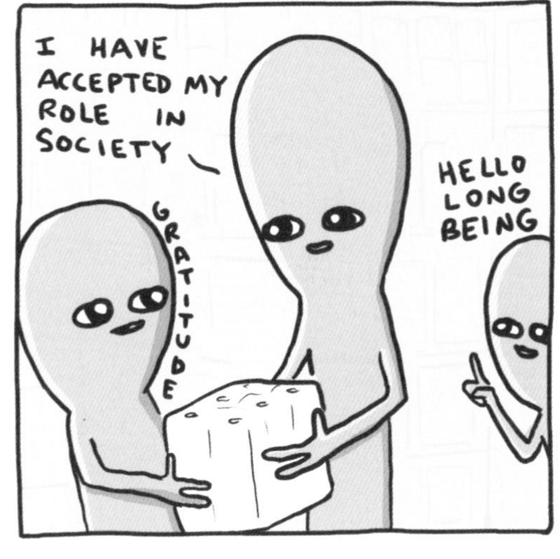
I HAVE ACCEPTED MY ROLE IN SOCIETY
GRATITUDE
HELLO LONG BEING

I AM GOING TO BECOME A BETTER BEING
WHEN

IN A FEW DAYS
OK

ON THE DAY WE TRADITIONALLY BECOME BETTER BEINGS
YES

UNTIL THEN I WILL MILDLY DEBASE MYSELF
TO MAXIMIZE CONTRAST
EXACTLY

WE CELEBRATE BECAUSE WE COMPLETED A REVOLUTION AROUND THE STAR

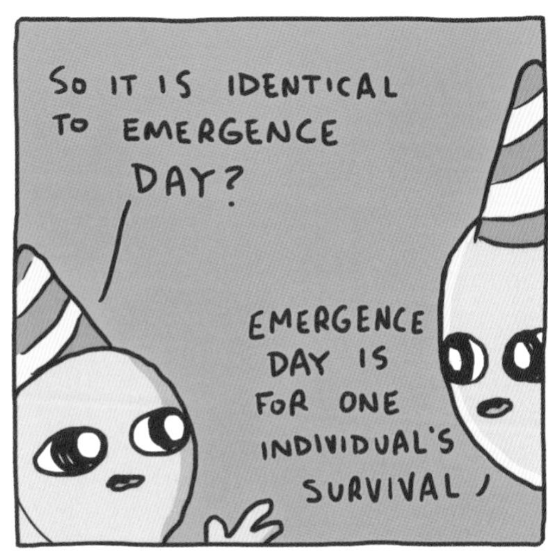
SO IT IS IDENTICAL TO EMERGENCE DAY?
EMERGENCE DAY IS FOR ONE INDIVIDUAL'S SURVIVAL

NEW REVOLUTION'S DAY CELEBRATES COLLECTIVE SURVIVAL
OH

WE DID NOT DIE
EXACTLY

I LOVE OBSERVING THE MASSIVE LIQUID
I COULD DO IT EVERY DAY

NATURE

THE CREATURE IS ERRATIC

IT OBEYS ONLY ITSELF

IT HAS FREEDOM TO EXPLORE THIS ENTIRE SPACE

YET PREFERS THE CONFINES OF A TINY BOX

INEXPLICABLE

WHAT A CURIOUS CREATURE

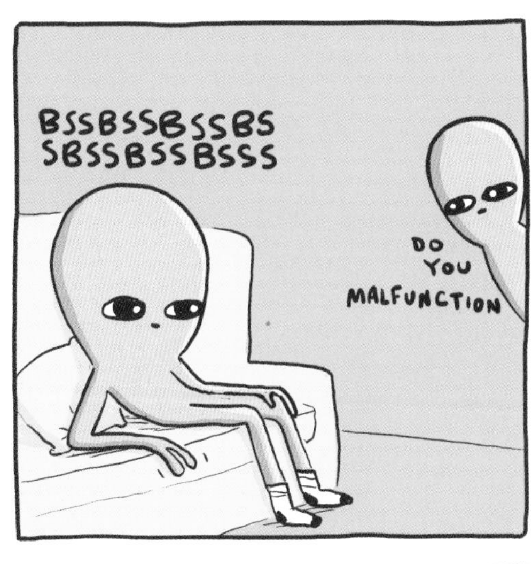
BSSBSSBSSBS
SBSSBSSBSSS
DO YOU MALFUNCTION

IT IS A VERBAL COAXING TECHNIQUE

WHAT WENT WRONG
THE CREATURE DISCOVERED MY SECRET INTENTION

FRIENDSHIP?
IT WAS TOO MUCH
I WAS PRESUMPTUOUS

THE CREATURE SEEKS OUT IMMEDIATE HYDRATION

I HAVE EMPTIED THE CYLINDER
IT WILL SEEK OTHER LIQUID

WHY

THE CREATURE IS ERRATIC
IT OBEYS ONLY ITSELF

THE CREATURE IS RUGGED AND FLEXIBLE
YES.
THUS IT IS LOGICAL THAT IT WOULD TREAT OTHER OBJECTS AS IF THEY ARE TOO
SUCH AS OUR HYDRATION CYLINDERS
ALSO OUR SKIN
EXACTLY

WHY DO YOUR ORIFICES OOZE?

MY BODY IS REACTING TO SOMETHING IN THESE FIBERS

THEN WHY ARE YOU TOUCHING THEM

BECAUSE WE'RE BEST FRIENDS

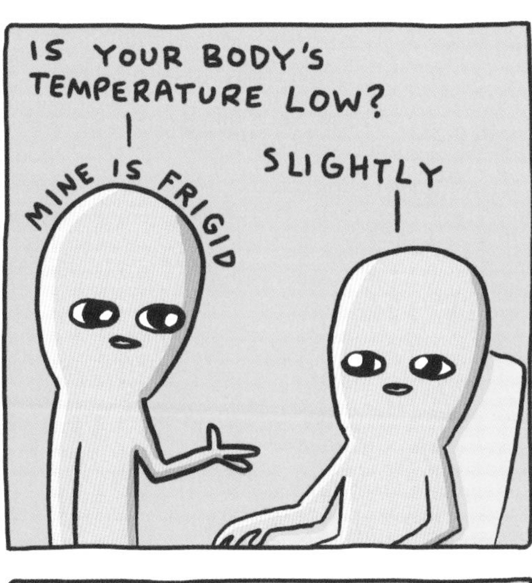
IS YOUR BODY'S TEMPERATURE LOW?
MINE IS FRIGID
SLIGHTLY

MY BODY'S TEMPERATURE IS SO LOW I CANNOT CONVEY IT VERBALLY
I BELIEVE THIS

I MUST PHYSICALLY DEMONSTRATE
I BELIEVED YOUR WORDS

ACKNOWLEDGE THE CONTRAST
THE CONTRAST IS STARK

WELL THE ATMOSPHERE'S UNPLEASANT

BUT THESE FLAMES ARE INCANDESCENT

SO IF THERE'S VAPOR IN THE SKIES

CRYSTALLIZE
CRYSTALLIZE
CRYSTALLIZE

I DISLIKE THESE ACCESSORIES
THEY ARE NECESSARY

WHY
BECAUSE OF THE ANGLE OF THE STAR'S LIGHT

I REQUEST WE REPOSITION
WELL...

MANY BEINGS LEARN TO ENJOY IT
WE MUST NOT RISK BECOMING THEM

WHAT ARE YOU DOING
I HAVE ACHIEVED PERFECT PHYSICAL WARMTH

IT IS IMPOSSIBLE FOR WARMTH TO ESCAPE MY HEAT CONTAINMENT FABRICS

MOVEMENT IS UNNECESSARY

I WILL NOW OBSERVE A PREDICTABLE NARRATIVE
FOR EMOTIONAL WARMTH?
YES

THIS ACTIVITY IS DANGEROUS BECAUSE OF THE SLICK SURFACE

TO MAKE IT SAFER WE STRAP BLADES TO OUR FEET
THAT MAKES SENSE

AND WE MOSTLY SLAP THIS OBJECT?
YES

BUT ALSO EACH OTHER
BOTH ARE IMPORTANT

THIS IS SCALDING
I WANT IT

IT APPEARS YOU POURED HOT LIQUID ON SOME OLD LEAVES

THAT'S EXACTLY WHAT I DID
MMM HOT LEAF LIQUID

SUCROSE CRYSTALS
SEVERAL THOUSAND PLEASE

THIS EQUIPMENT WILL CONTAIN THE OFFSPRING AND FREE UP OUR LIMBS

AND THUS ALLOWS US TO CARRY THE ITEMS THE OFFSPRING NEEDS

THE OFFSPRING IS DOMINATING OUR LIMB USE
WE NEED MORE LIMBS

WE MADE MORE LIMBS
THEY ARE NOT YET USEFUL

I AM EMBARKING ON A RESPONSIBILITY ESCAPE. WILL YOU BE A COMPANION TO MY CREATURE?
YES I WILL DO THIS

I TREASURE YOU AND WILL OBSERVE YOU SOON.

DO NOT BE SAD. I AM HERE TO BEFRIEND YOU.

HOW IS MY CREATURE?
ALOOF AND INDIFFERENT
THAT'S MY PRECIOUS CREATURE

MY CREATURE!
I RETURNED.
APPROACH ME

OK I WILL APPROACH

WHY ARE YOU CONSCIOUS

RETURN TO UNCONSCIOUSNESS
WHY MUST I
YOUR BODY IS GROWING

BUT YOU ARE BOTH CONSCIOUS
OUR BODIES ARE IN DECLINE

THAT IS UNSETTLING
FOR US TOO
PLEASE BE KIND TO US

IT
SLITHERS

RELAX
NEVER

THIS CREATURE'S FEAR OF YOU
EXCEEDS YOUR FEAR OF IT
WE ARE
THE ONLY
CREATURE WHO
SAYS THIS

AND
YOU WILDLY
UNDERASSESS
MY FEAR

I LOVE OBSERVING THE MASSIVE LIQUID

I COULD OBSERVE IT EVERY DAY

THE EXPERIENCE IS STILL NOVEL FOR ME BECAUSE OF WHERE I LIVED AS A YOUNG BEING

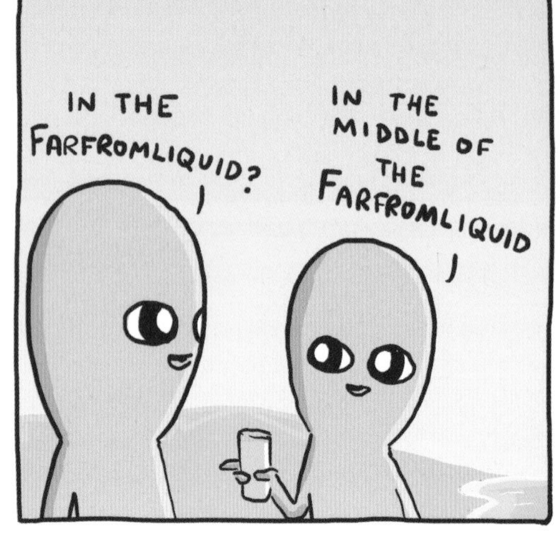
IN THE FARFROMLIQUID?
IN THE MIDDLE OF THE FARFROMLIQUID

WHAT ARE YOU INGESTING
IT'S AN ENERGY ROD

OBSERVE THE STRENUOUS ACTION DEPICTED

DO YOU PLAN TO SCALE RUGGED TERRAIN
YES

THE RUGGED TERRAIN OF DAILY EXISTENCE
FAIR

MAY I BEFRIEND YOUR CREATURE
YOU MAY

I WILL NOW REQUEST ALL INFORMATION ABOUT THEM
MY EXPERTISE

TO ME YOUR EXISTENCE IS CENTERED ONLY ON THIS CREATURE

AN ACCURATE STATEMENT

ADJACENT TO YOUR MEAL DO YOU DESIRE THE HOT OIL STARCH STICKS OR THE LEAF BUCKET?
I...

I DESIRE LEAVES

WHO ARE YOU

THIS CREATURE HAS PERISHED
YES

IT PERISHED LONG AGO
BUT IT HAS BEEN PARTIALLY REASSEMBLED

THIS SAYS THAT IT PERISHED PERMANENTLY
IT IS UNLIKELY FOR THIS LIFE FORM TO EXIST AGAIN

BUT SOMETIMES
EXISTENCE LOCATES A PATH

BUT HOW COULD EXISTENCE LOCATE A PATH
IT DOES SEEM IMPOSSIBLE

BUT INTELLIGENT BEINGS MAY ONE DAY SOLVE THIS PROBLEM WITH SCIENCE

BUT WOULDN'T SOME OF THESE LARGE CREATURES WANT TO CONSUME US?

THIS WOULD BE A SECOND MORE INTERESTING PROBLEM

IS THIS SANITARY
IT IS AFFECTION

THIS IS ILLOGICAL
THE CREATURE ADORES ME

THE CREATURE INGESTS UNKNOWN OBJECTS
WHAT DO YOU IMPLY

THE CREATURE HAS LOW STANDARDS
THE CREATURE CAN HEAR YOU
AGAIN ILLOGICAL

WE MUST CONVINCE THE CREATURE TO YELL AT FEWER THINGS
I LOCATED A SOLUTION

THIS PASTE MAKES THE CREATURE CEASE YELLING
IS IT SAFE?
YES I INGESTED A SIGNIFICANT AMOUNT MYSELF

IT IS EFFECTIVE UNTIL IT FINISHES AND REQUESTS MORE
HOW DOES THE CREATURE REQUEST MORE

IT YELLS AT ME
SO MUCH YELLING

THE CREATURE MORTALLY WOUNDED THIS PLAY OBJECT WITH UNNERVING VIGOR

...THEN PRESENTED IT TO ME
PERHAPS IT IS A GIFT

EACH DAY WE ARE IN CLOSE PROXIMITY TO A HIGHLY EFFICIENT PREDATOR

YET WE SURVIVE
ANOTHER GIFT

OBSERVE!

THE CREATURE CLEANSES ITSELF

RECIPROCAL OBSERVATION

HIIII

I MISS
THAT
CREATURE

OBSERVE! THIS CREATURE IS A FRIEND

AS IS THIS CREATURE
WHY

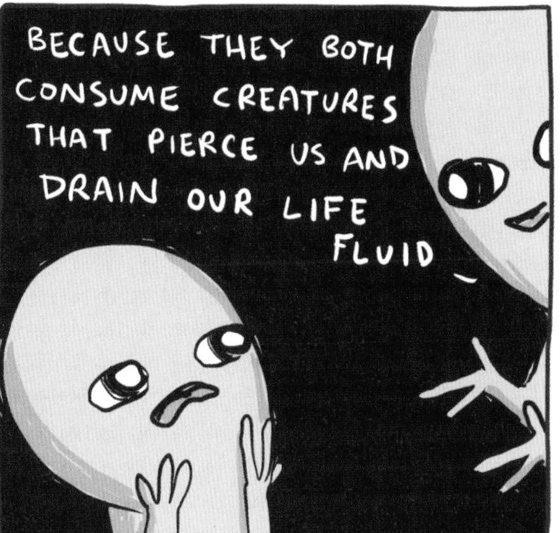
BECAUSE THEY BOTH CONSUME CREATURES THAT PIERCE US AND DRAIN OUR LIFE FLUID

EXISTENCE IS TERRIFYING
AT LEAST WE HAVE FRIENDS

EMOTIONS

WILDLY UNPREPARED FOR THE DAY

I HAVE REMOVED THE SUPPLEMENTAL WHEELS
I SENSE INCREASED INSTABILITY

ACTUALLY YOU SENSE INSTABILITY THAT WAS ALWAYS PRESENT BUT THAT YOU WERE UNAWARE OF. THIS WILL BE A COMMON EXPERIENCE AS YOU AGE
WHAT

I AM GOING TO SHOVE YOU
OK

COMMENCE THE DANGER

ARE YOU ABLE TO ASSIST ME WITH ARITHMETIC
THE ANSWER IS UNKNOWN

I FEEL SADNESS AND LACK UNDERSTANDING
WE CAN FEEL THAT TOGETHER

DID YOU COMPLETE THIS COURSE
MANY REVOLUTIONS AGO

ARE THE MEMORIES OF THE COURSE RETURNING
SO FAR ONLY THE EMOTIONS

THIS IS DISPROPORTIONATE

WHAT IS OCCURRING
JUSTICE

WHAT
SEMICONSCIOUS SELFISHNESS IS STILL SELFISHNESS

YOU CHOSE A COMPLICATED SUSTENANCE FORMULA
IT WAS A MISTAKE

ARE YOU MISSING A NECESSARY COMPONENT

YES
SUSTAINED MOTIVATION

WHAT PHASE ARE YOU IN
REGRET

MY HOME
MY
REGULATIONS
SWEET DISKS

SWEET DISKS

EW
SWEET DISKS

LIFEGIVER
YOU WERE
CORRECT

ELEVATED HANDSLAP!

NOW
DESCEND

INSUFFICIENT SPEED!
MEANINGLESS DECEPTION

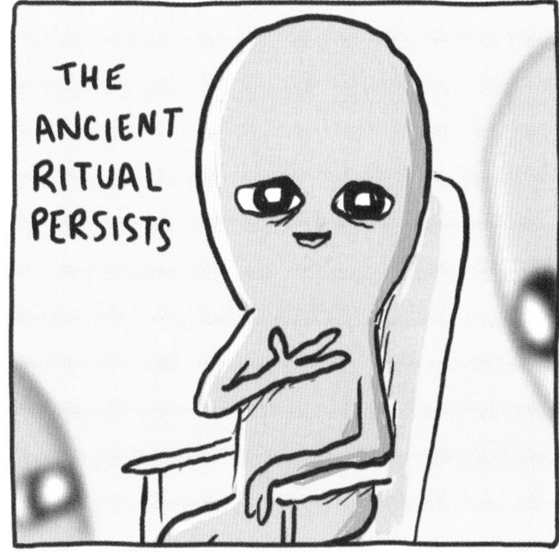
THE ANCIENT RITUAL PERSISTS

IF I CONSUME TOO MUCH OF THIS JITTER LIQUID IT IRRITATES MY STORAGE ORGAN

ARE YOU NEAR YOUR LIMIT NOW
NO

I EXCEEDED MY LIMIT EARLIER

I JUST HEAVED THE HEAVIEST OBJECT I HAVE EVER HEAVED
HOW FAR DID YOU MOVE IT

IT IS BACK WHERE I FOUND IT
CONSIDERATE

I ALSO CLEANSED IT
EXEMPLARY BEHAVIOR

OBSERVE MY EXPANSION
YOU WILD FEROCIOUS CREATURE

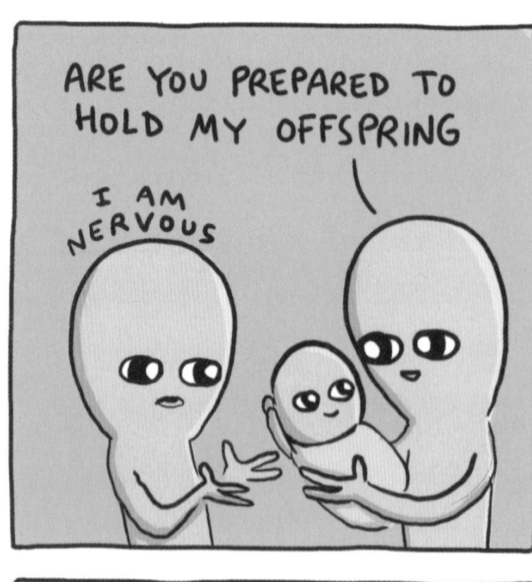
ARE YOU PREPARED TO HOLD MY OFFSPRING
I AM NERVOUS

I AM UNSURE OF PROPER TECHNIQUES
I SAY THAT EVERY DAY

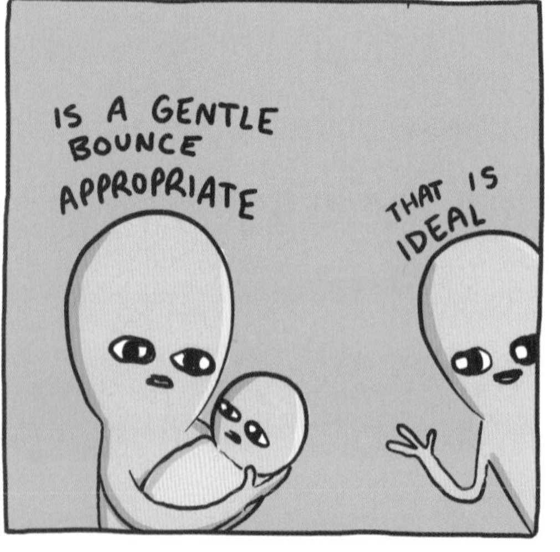
IS A GENTLE BOUNCE APPROPRIATE
THAT IS IDEAL

OUR MUTUAL UNEASE INCREASES
NO NO THIS IS BONDING

OBSERVE MY PROGRESS!
MAYBE THIS IS NOT SO DIFFICULT

AND I MUST ACCOMPLISH THIS ONCE A DAY?
MULTIPLE TIMES

HOW COULD ANY BEING ACHIEVE THIS?

I ALSO ASK THIS EVERY DAY

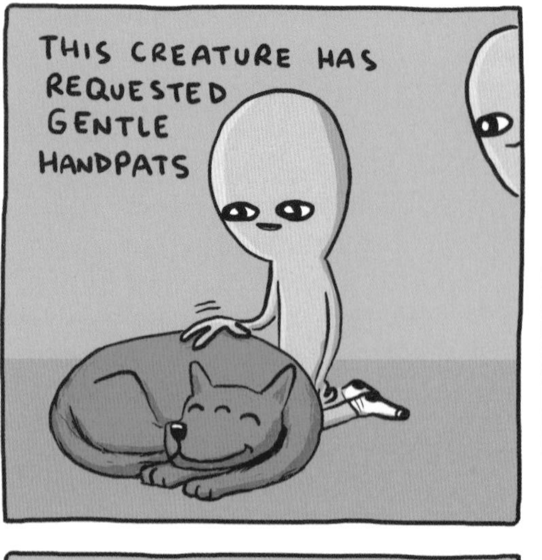
THIS CREATURE HAS REQUESTED GENTLE HANDPATS

FOR HOW LONG

UNTIL ONE OF US PERISHES
A LIFE WELL SPENT

DO YOU REQUIRE ASSISTANCE
NO

I BELIEVE IN MY ABILITIES
I OBSERVE

BUT A SECOND JOURNEY WOUL-
THERE CANNOT BE A SECOND JOURNEY

OK
I NEED THE THRILL OF EFFICIENCY

I AM COMPELLED TO COMPLETE THIS SPIRAL

THE CONCENTRIC PATTERN MUST BE PERFECT

I FEEL BOTH PRIDE AND SHAME
WOW

THE COST IS IMMENSE
I ASSUMED

I WAS UNCONSCIOUS FOR LONGER THAN PLANNED

THIS WORK IS INCOMPLETE

I HAVE NO SKY SHIELD

HOW ARE YOU
WILDLY UNPREPARED FOR THE DAY

WE WISH TO PURCHASE 2 HOURS OF SUSTENANCE
WE WILL HOLD IT ON OUR THIGHS

PERHAPS A GRAIN RECEPTACLE?
I HAVE JUST EXPLODED THEM
IDEAL

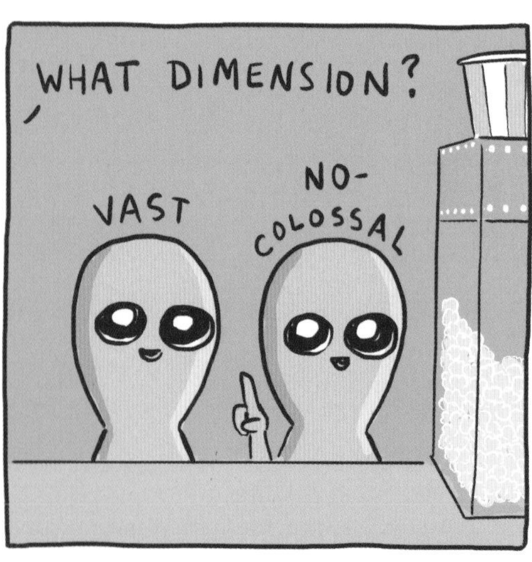
WHAT DIMENSION?
VAST
NO-
COLOSSAL

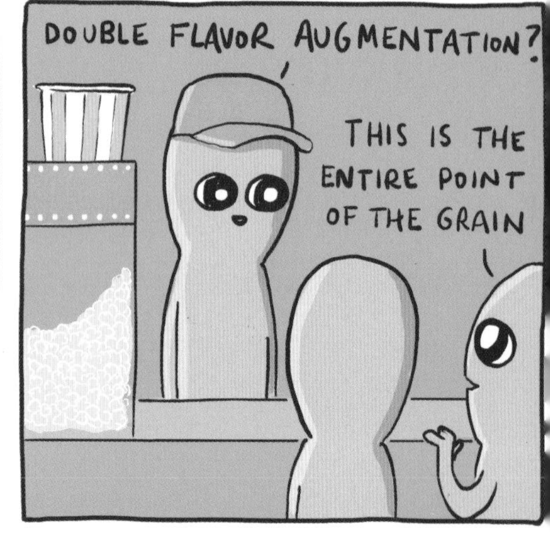
DOUBLE FLAVOR AUGMENTATION?
THIS IS THE ENTIRE POINT OF THE GRAIN

A CHARMING AGED STRUCTURE
SECLUDED IN VEGETATION

SHOULD WE INVESTIGATE THE INTERIOR
I OBSERVE NO REASON AGAINST IT

TRUE - WHAT NEGATIVE OUTCOME COULD THERE BE?

SO MANY NEGATIVE OUTCOMES
THEY ARE NOT LOGICAL

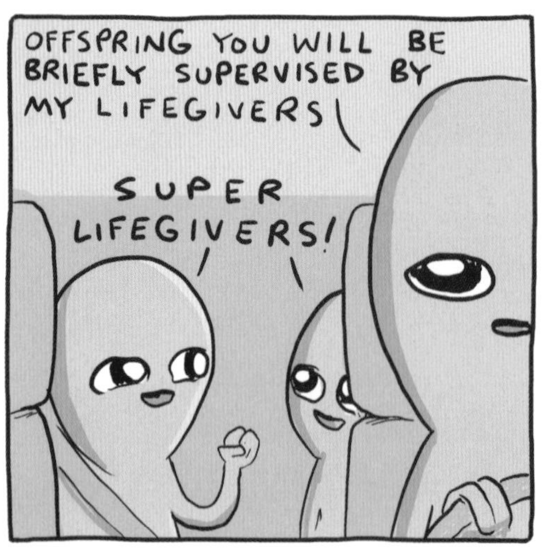
OFFSPRING YOU WILL BE BRIEFLY SUPERVISED BY MY LIFEGIVERS
SUPER LIFEGIVERS!

VOW TO BE COMPLIANT
WE VOW

MAY WE
ABSOLUTELY
ANYTHING

YOU DESERVE THIS
SWEET SWEET INFANTS

OBSERVE MY ACTION SIMULATION
I WILL BE IMPRESSED BY WHATEVER YOU DO
AH I TUMBLED OFF OF A CLIFF AND I PERISHED
WOW
WE ARE SO PROUD

AS A YOUNGLING WE DID NOT HAVE THESE SIMULATIONS
REALLY?

IF YOU TUMBLED OFF A CLIFF YOU ACTUALLY PERISHED
WHOA
BRUTAL

ARE YOU IN EMOTIONAL DISTRESS
NO
I AM PRETENDING TO BE A SORROWFUL BEING BECAUSE I HAVE A PORTRAYAL COMPETITION TODAY

I CANNOT DISTINGUISH YOUR THEATRICAL SADNESS FROM YOUR GENUINE SADNESS
THEY ARE TRULY BLENDING

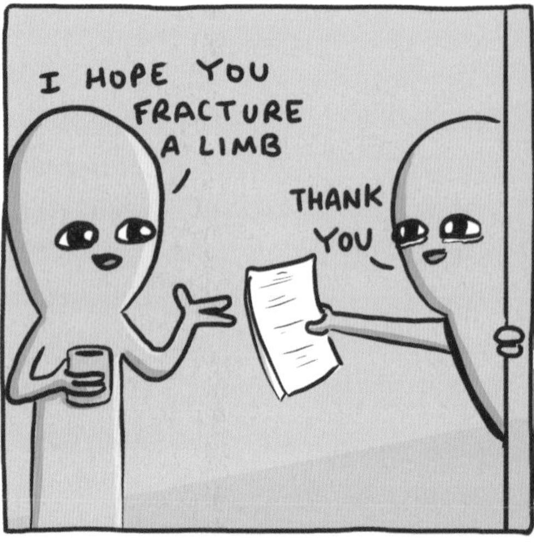

I HOPE YOU FRACTURE A LIMB
THANK YOU

WHICH BEING ARE YOU HERE TO PORTRAY?

THE MOURNFUL BEING
ME TOO!

I THINK YOU WILL BE EXTREMELY SAD TODAY
I THINK YOUR SORROW WILL SURPASS MINE!

I HOPE YOU'RE DEVASTATED
I HOPE YOU ARE INCONSOLABLE

I DO NOT RECALL OPENING THIS PORTAL

WAS THIS DONE BY A TRANSLUCENT PERISHED BEING?

THIS IS THE LEAST REASONABLE EXPLANATION

...THAT I AM NOW OBSESSED WITH
WHAT DO THEY DESIRE

I WILL NOW RELAY AN ANECDOTE
OH NO

I WILL ATTEMPT TO RECALL ALL DETAILS
DO NOT PROCEED

EVERY DETAIL IS CRUCIAL
THIS IS NOT TRUE

THIS OCCURRED A FEW REVOLUTIONS AGO. IT MAY HAVE BEEN THREE REVOLUTIONS BUT MORE LIKELY IT WAS FOUR.
INCONSEQUENTIAL

THIS SCENT IS REPULSIVE

MAY I SHARE A SENSORY EXPERIENCE WITH YOU
WHAT WILL OCCUR IF I SAY YES

WE BOND IN MUTUAL DISGUST
WHAT DECAY IS THIS

SHARED NEGATIVE EXPERIENCES STRENGTHEN FRIENDSHIPS
I FEEL WEAKER THOUGH

OK BEINGS! NOW PUT 2 DIGITS ON YOUR NECK TO CALCULATE YOUR BLOODPUMP RATE

BUT WHY
IF WE INCREASE OUR RATE, WE DECREASE OUR ODDS OF PERISHING

I HOPE WE HIT MAXIMUM RATE
NO-IF WE HIT MAXIMUM RATE WE COULD PERISH

WE PERISH IN EITHER SCENARIO
WE PERISH IN EVERY SCENARIO

ARE YOU ENTHUSED ABOUT FORMAL EDUCATION
NO
MARVELOUS BEING

CAN YOU FEIGN ENTHUSIASM
WHY MUST I FEIGN ENTHUSIASM
MARVELOUS BEING

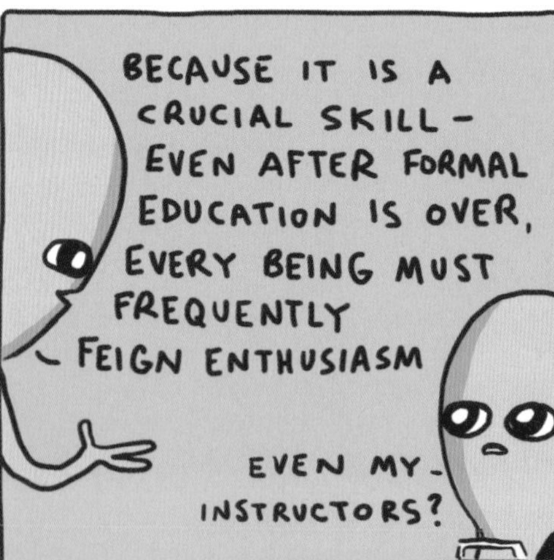
BECAUSE IT IS A CRUCIAL SKILL – EVEN AFTER FORMAL EDUCATION IS OVER, EVERY BEING MUST FREQUENTLY FEIGN ENTHUSIASM
EVEN MY – INSTRUCTORS?

ESPECIALLY YOUR INSTRUCTORS

REMEMBER, OFFSPRING-
IF YOU LACK THE TIME
TO EXECUTE A TASK PROPERLY THE FIRST TIME

THAT IS NORMAL-
WELCOME TO LIFE AS A GROWN BEING
WHAT

GROWN BEINGS MUST CHOOSE WHICH TASKS THEY WANT TO DO INCORRECTLY

IS THIS... WISDOM
NO-
THIS IS INFORMATION

SHALL WE CONTINUE THIS SERIES
AH IT CONTINUED AUTONOMOUSLY

THIS TECHNOLOGY EXPLOITS OUR APATHY
WE LACK THE WILL TO PAUSE IT

OUR RESTRAINT HAS BEEN OVERCOME
YET I AM NOT SAD

I'LL EXPLODE MORE GRAINS
I'LL PAUSE IT WHILE YOU DO

I RAMMED MY FOOT INTO A STATIONARY OBJECT
OH BEING
I HAVE BEEN TO THIS LOCATION

I FEEL SO IGNORANT
DO NOT FEEL IGNORANT - I SLICED MYSELF WITH A DOCUMENT
UGH DOCUMENT SLICES

I CHOMPED MY OWN FLAVORMUSCLE
YOUCH
THE MOST INFERIOR!

I DON'T KNOW HOW TO USE MY LIFE
A SLIGHTLY DIFFERENT EXAMPLE
BUT WE CAN ASSOCIATE

THIS IS THE VOID.
WE CALL IT VOID NOT
BECAUSE WE KNOW IT
IS EMPTY BUT BECAUSE
WE DO NOT KNOW WHAT
IT IS FULL OF.

KNOWLEDGE

CHAOS IS HOW I LEARN

I RECALLED TRIVIAL KNOWLEDGE THAT NONE OF THESE BEINGS KNEW
IT FEELS GOOD TO KNOW A FACT BUT EVEN BETTER WHEN OTHERS DO NOT KNOW IT
I NEVER CONSIDERED THIS
THANK YOU - THAT FEELS FANTASTIC
YOU ARE WELCOME

YOU HAVE BEEN CORRECT THRICE CONSECUTIVELY

AND YET I AM AWARDED NO CURRENCY

THEIR REWARD MAY BE CURRENCY - BUT YOURS IS KNOWLEDGE

I'D RATHER HAVE CURRENCY
THIS IS SELF-KNOWLEDGE

IT'S AN ANCIENT LIGHT SOURCE
THANK YOU

YOU NEED A SECOND TOOL TO TURN IT ON
OK

NOT SUPER BRIGHT
UNLESS YOU KNOCK IT OVER AND IT DESTROYS ALL IT TOUCHES
WOW

SMELLS LIKE SUSTENANCE
IT'S NOT

I HAVE GIVEN MY FACE NEW TOPOGRAPHY

HOW
I LEARNED FROM THIS BEING WHO CAN TRANSFORM INTO ANY BEING

THIS BEING IS A FRIEND?
NO I HAVE NEVER MET THIS BEING

OR HAVE YOU
OR HAVE I

THIS IS THE VOID. WE CALL IT VOID NOT BECAUSE WE KNOW IT IS EMPTY BUT BECAUSE WE DO NOT KNOW WHAT IT IS FULL OF

WHAT

YOU MUST BE CAREFUL
IN THE VOID
IF YOU'RE NOT, YOU'LL
BE DESTROYED

YOU CAN'T INHALE
YOU'LL GET TOO COLD
THE AMBIANCE IS
UNCONTROLLED

YOU NEED A VESSEL
YOU CAN STEER
YOU NEED SOME SPECIAL
VOID-PROOF GEAR

WE'VE NOT GONE FAR
THIS MUCH IS TRUE-
TO EXPLORE MORE?
IT'S UP TO YOU!

WHAT IS THE CRUCIAL REGULATION?
NO HANDS ON ORB

WHAT IF THE ORB APPROACHES OUR FACE?
LET THE ORB SMACK YOUR FACE

WHO IS THE ONE BEING WHOSE HANDS TOUCH THE ORB?
THE ORBHANDLER
OBSERVE THE HANDCOVERS
IT IS A LONELY ROLE

LET US PUT HANDS TOGETHER
1...2..3 CAN'T USE THESE

HERE IS A BRIEF INTERMISSION MESSAGE:
IT IS OK THAT THEY ARE NETTING THE ORB MORE THAN US

...STILL, WE SHOULD MAKE AN EFFORT TO NET THE ORB AT LEAST ONCE

SO WE NEED ELEVEN TENTHS FROM ALL OF YOU
WE HAVE ONLY TEN
ILLOGICAL
WE NEED ELEVEN

NOW INGEST THE TRADITIONAL FRUCTOSE

THIS MACHINE GIVES YOU CURRENCY
FANTASTIC

BUT ONLY IF YOU HAVE CURRENCY
DEVASTATING

IT TELLS YOU HOW MUCH CURRENCY YOU HAVE
I WILL NOT WANT TO KNOW

TOUCH HERE TO SEE THE NUMBER
I WILL NOT TOUCH IT THERE

MY ROLLMACHINE IS NOT ROLLING WHEN I ASK IT TO
AH ITS PRIMARY FUNCTION

I ATTEMPTED TO LOCATE THE MALFUNCTION
AND?
IT HAPPENED IN THE COMPLICATED ZONE

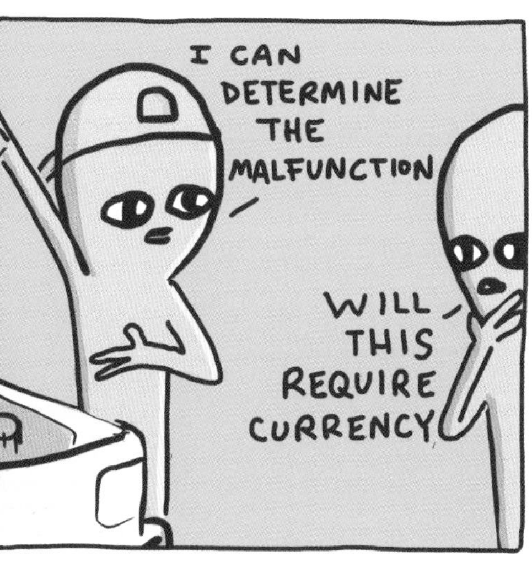
I CAN DETERMINE THE MALFUNCTION
WILL THIS REQUIRE CURRENCY

EXPERTISE ALWAYS DOES
I SHOULD HAVE CONSULTED A NOVICE

WHAT IS THE PURPOSE OF THIS?
FOR THE GROUP: ENTERTAINMENT
FRIENDS
CONTRIVED!

BUT INDIVIDUALLY: DOMINATION
INFERIORS
CONTRIVED!

ARE YOU CONFIDENT YOU UNDERSTAND?
FOR ME, IGNORANCE IS CONFIDENCE
CONTRIVED!

THEN YOU WILL LOSE VALIANTLY
IT WILL BE BITTERSWEET
CONTRIVED!

OBSERVE -
THEY FLY IN CIRCLES BEFORE CONSUMING A PERISHED CREATURE

WILL THEY CONSUME US?
ONLY IF WE PERISH

DO NOT FRET - MANY CREATURES ARE HOPING WE PERISH
UH

VERY FEW ARE WILLING TO MAKE IT HAPPEN
OK

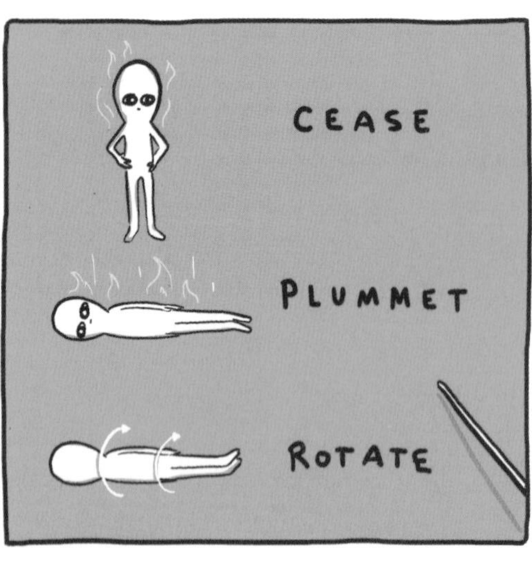
CEASE
PLUMMET
ROTATE

ROTATE UNTIL YOU ARE EXTINGUISHED
CEASE
PLUMMET
ROTATE

HOW FREQUENTLY WILL WE DO THIS
ALMOST CERTAINLY NEVER

BUT YOU WILL RECALL THIS UNTIL THE DAY YOU PERISH
OK

I HAVE A NEW PRODUCTIVE DIVERSION
WHAT WILL IT PRODUCE

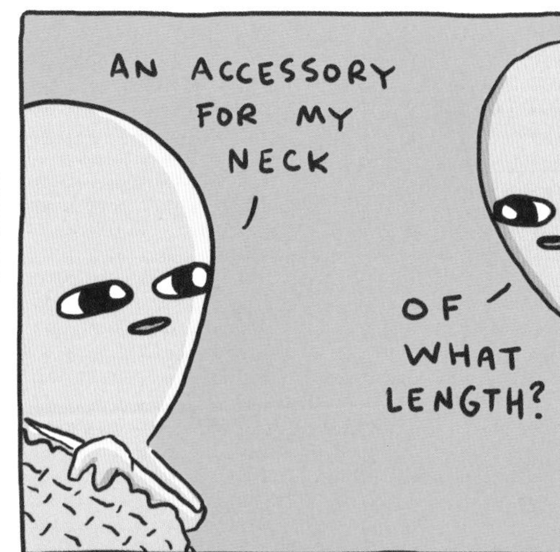
AN ACCESSORY FOR MY NECK
OF WHAT LENGTH?

ANY LENGTH I DESIRE. THERE ARE NO REGULATIONS

CONSTRUCTIVE LAWLESSNESS
THE ONLY RISK IS EXCESSIVE WARMTH

YOUNG BEINGS, TODAY WE WILL DISCUSS VARIOUS MEASUREMENTS
10
1
1
10

LONG AGO, BEINGS CREATED A LOGICAL SYSTEM THAT IS BASED ON DECIMALS
1
1
10

DO ALL BEINGS USE THIS SYSTEM?
THERE IS A SMALL PERCENTAGE OF BEINGS WHO DON'T

DO THEY NOT KNOW ABOUT THE LOGICAL SYSTEM?
NO THEY DEFINITELY KNOW

BUT WHY IS THE NUMBER TEN? IS THAT THE LOGICAL NUMBER?
UH

THE NUMBER TEN IS BASED ON OUR HANDS AND FEET

3
3
2
2
3 + 3 + 2 + 2 =
10

...SO IT'S LOGICAL IF YOU ARE A BEING
WELL WE ARE

AS THE STAR BEGINS TO FADE,
PREPARATIONS
MUST BE MADE

SUSTENANCE WE MUST PREPARE
SO WE CAN EACH CONSUME
OUR SHARE

THESE THREE OBJECTS WILL
SUFFICE
FOR US TO SCOOP
AND STAB
AND SLICE

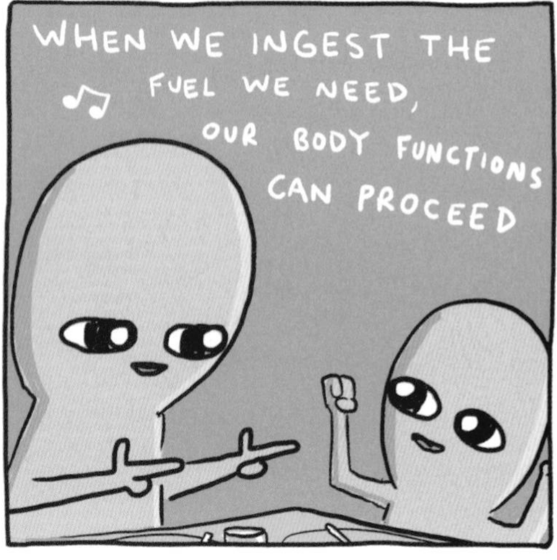
WHEN WE INGEST THE
FUEL WE NEED,
OUR BODY FUNCTIONS
CAN PROCEED

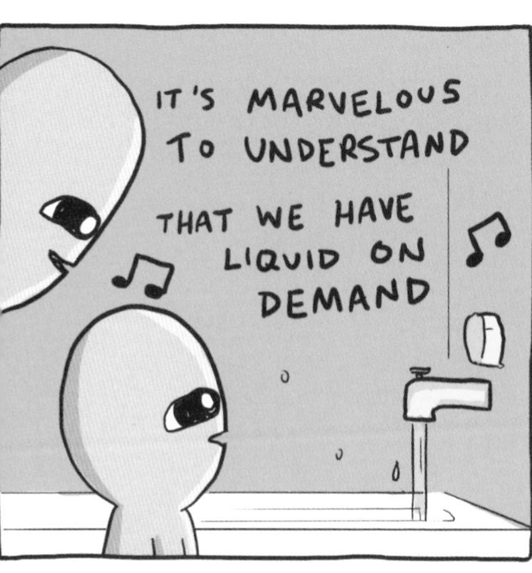
IT'S MARVELOUS TO UNDERSTAND
THAT WE HAVE LIQUID ON DEMAND

IT STARTS OUT AT A NATURAL SOURCE
IT TRAVELS WITH IMPRESSIVE FORCE

IT COMES RIGHT OUT WITHOUT DELAY
IT TRANSPORTS ALL OUR FILTH AWAY

OUR USE OF LIQUID IS ADVANCED
AND NOW WE SMELL LIKE LOVELY PLANTS

WHOA
ARE YOU PERISHING
CURF CURF

ARE MY HANDSLAPS SAVING YOU
SMACK SMACK SMACK

YOU DID NOT SAVE ME - I MERELY SENT LIQUID DOWN MY GAS TUNNEL
OK

THE SPASMS WERE A NATURAL REACTION
OK
SO WERE MY HANDSLAPS

WE WILL PAY YOU TO LET US SING AS BADLY AS WE WANT

I WILL AMPLIFY YOUR VOICES IN AN INSULATED CHAMBER

PERFECT BECAUSE ONLY OUR FRIENDS WILL WANT TO HEAR THIS
I KNOW I DON'T

OHHH I WANT TO FLAIL WITH A BEING
I NORMALLY LOVE THIS MELODY

WHY DO WE OBSERVE THE ORB-CATCHERS IF IT MAKES US SO SAD

WE DIDN'T -KNOW- IT WOULD
WE JUST KNEW IT WAS LIKELY TO

STATISTICALLY MOST OBSERVERS EXPERIENCE GENERAL SADNESS AT THE END...
...BUT THIS IS ABOUT JOINING A GROUP OF BEINGS TO BE SPECIFICALLY SAD WITH

UNIQUE PAIN
IN PARTICULAR HATS

OBSERVE: DO ANY BEINGS HERE REMEMBER THE TIME WE WERE THIS CLOSE TO ULTIMATE HAPPINESS

I WAS THERE WHEN WE DROPPED THE ORB
MY FACE LEAKED FOR DAYS

ISN'T THIS FUN
HOW CAN I BE INCLUDED

CAN YOU WITHSTAND DISAPPOINTMENT?
I DID TONIGHT
A GOOD START

THERE IS A DOCUMENT ON MY SUSTENANCE
THIS SEEMS UNUSUAL

THERE IS NO DOCUMENT ON MINE
YOU LIKELY INGESTED IT

WILL THIS BE TOXIC?
IT IS LIKELY HARMLESS
YET YOU WILL NOT INGEST YOURS

IF IT IS TOXIC ONE OF US MUST SURVIVE TO INFORM OTHERS
FAIR

WHAT IS YOUR DISCUSSION?
WE ARE NOT CERTAIN IF IT IS SAFE TO INGEST DOCUMENTS

ILLOGICAL. IT IS EASY TO AVOID.
THEY ARE ADHERED TO OUR SUSTENANCE

THIS MAKES IT DIFFICULT TO AVOID
IS THIS HOW I PERISH

IT IS A SMALL DOCUMENT YOU WILL SURVIVE
I WILL NOT INGEST LARGER
GOOD RESTRAINT

PROPEL THE ORB UP THERE
A LONGER BODY WOULD ASSIST ME

YOUR BODY IS UNLIKELY TO BE LONG BECAUSE MINE IS NOT LONG

THIS IS DISAPPOINTING BUT I WILL NOT ALLOW IT TO DIVERT MY FOCUS

GOOD EMOTIONAL REGULATION - ALSO FROM ME

I'M CONCERNED A HOSTILE CREATURE WILL SUDDENLY APPEAR
WHAT DO WE SAY?

THERE IS NO EVIDENCE TO SUPPORT THIS CONCERN
...BUT

...IF I GATHER NEW EVIDENCE WE COULD REVISE OUR CONCLUSION
CORRECT

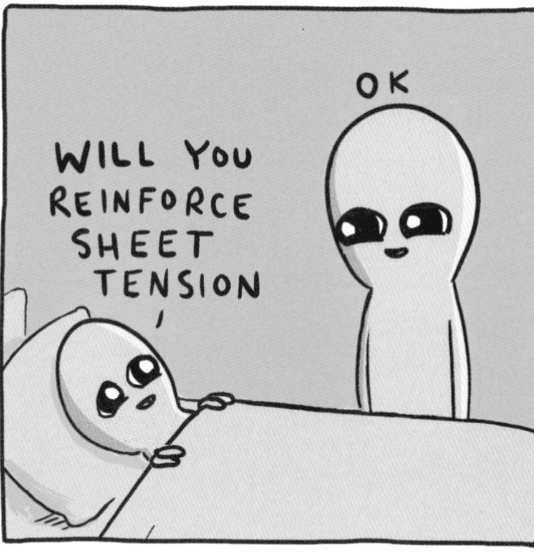
WILL YOU REINFORCE SHEET TENSION
OK

HERE IS THE BEING YOU MANEUVER. THIS BEING IS A DRAINAGE EXPERT.

OBTAIN THE FUNGUS. IT WILL INCREASE YOUR MASS.
OK

THIS PLANT WILL ALLOW YOU TO PROPEL FIRE!
WHOA HOW DO YOU KNOW ALL THIS?

I HAVE DEVOTED MUCH OF MY LIFE TO STUDYING THIS BEING'S LORE

I HAVE ATTEMPTED SCIENCE
PLEASE EXPLAIN

I FORMED AN IDEA AND THEN DISCOVERED I WAS WRONG.

THERE ARE NUMEROUS DIAGRAMS
I WAS WRONG IN NUMEROUS WAYS

I PRODUCED A DETAILED TRIBUTE TO MY WRONGNESS
THAT IS SCIENCE

THIS STRUCTURE IS FULL OF TEXTS
FOR US TO PURCHASE
NO. WE SIMPLY TAKE

THIS IS INCREDIBLE BY WHICH I MEAN DIFFICULT TO BELIEVE
OBSERVE THIS

I BRIEFLY POSSESSED THIS THOUGH I DID NOT READ IT
THERE IS NO SHAME
TEXTS

THERE ARE NO EXPECTATIONS
THEY EXPECT YOU TO RETURN THEM
IT IS THE CORE CONCEPT

GREETINGS—
I HAD TO SEND YOU MORE CURRENCY THAN USUAL
AND I WANTED TO ASK WHY

YOU OBSERVED TOO MUCH ON YOUR DEVICE.
I SUGGEST YOU UPGRADE FROM "OBSERVE MANY THINGS" TO THE "OBSERVE EVERYTHING" PLAN

OK THIS SEEMS WISE.
I LOVE TO OBSERVE AND THEN TRANSMIT WHAT I HAVE OBSERVED TO MY FRIENDS

EXCELLENT!
THIS PLAN ALSO INCLUDES INFINITE TIME INCREMENTS TO SPEAK TO THOSE FRIENDS
THANK YOU I WILL NOT NEED THIS PART

OH NO I HAVE CREAMY FLUID LEFT AND NOW REQUIRE A SWEET DISK

OH NO HALF A SWEET DISK LEFT AND NOW NEED CREAMY FLUID

OH NOOOOOOO

DO YOU LIKE THE BOOK?
WE'RE ENJOYING THE NARRATIVE

IT'S DELIGHTFUL TO IMAGINE BEINGS ON A DIFFERENT PLANET WHO ARE SIMILAR TO US
COOL RIGHT?

HAHA YES... COOL
WE LOVE THE STUFF THEY SAY

IT FRACTURES US
CRACKS US UP
IT CRACKS US UP
NICE

DO YOU THINK THEY LOOK LIKE US?
WELL
UH

THEIR HEADS ARE TINY, YEAH?
I WASN'T GOING TO SAY IT

WE LOVE THEIR SMALL HEADS
AND THEIR MANY DIGITS

WE FIND THEM ADORABLE
WE WANT THEM TO EXIST
SAME HERE

COMMONLY OBSERVED OBJECTS & BEINGS

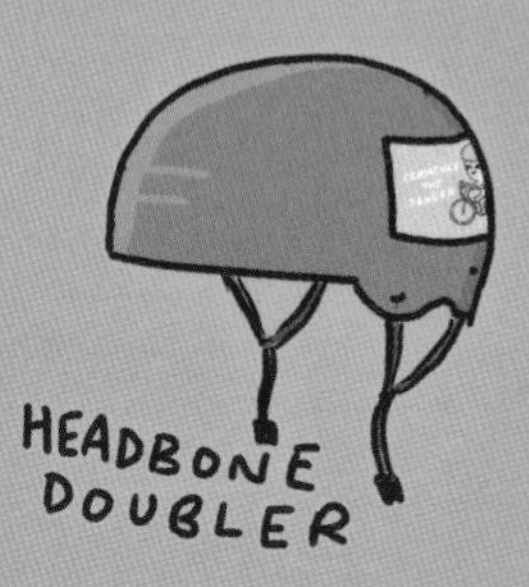

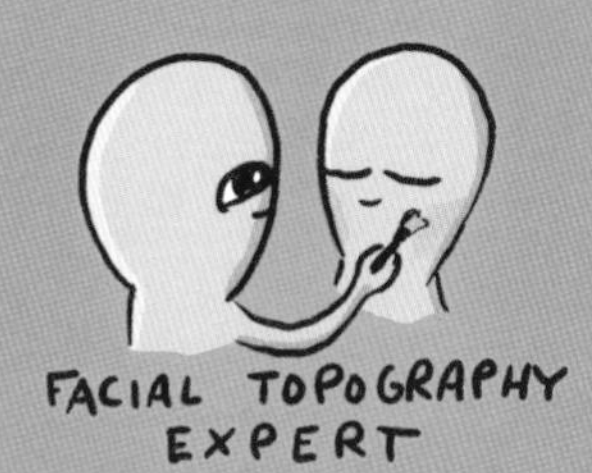

COMMONLY OBSERVED OBJECTS & BEINGS

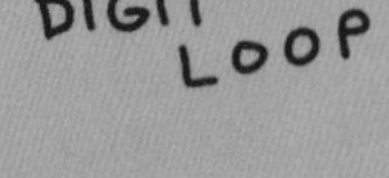

DIGIT LOOP

COMMITMENT TO COHESION

MILD POISON

ROLLMACHINE

GROUPROLLMACHINE

ROLLMACHINE EXPERT

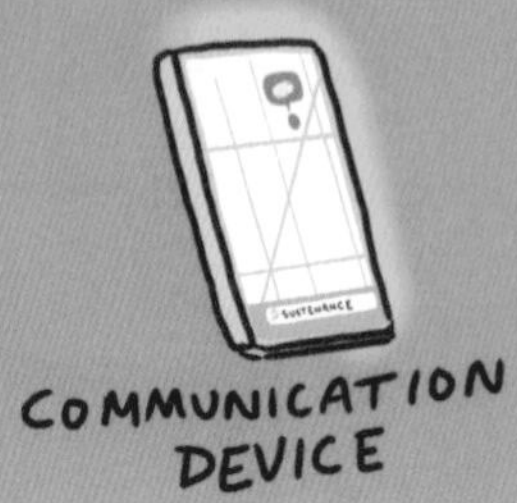

COMMUNICATION DEVICE

SUSTENANCE LOCATOR

SWADDLED SUSTENANCE

COMMONLY OBSERVED OBJECTS & BEINGS

COMPLEX JITTER LIQUID

JITTER LIQUID EXPERT

PLANTSCENTLIQUID

STABBER

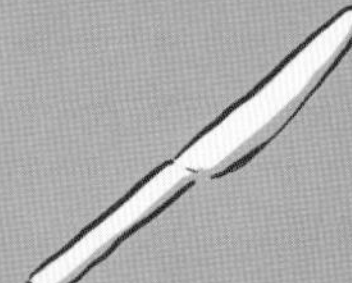

SLICER

SCOOPER

BEHIND-BAG

ERRATIC CREATURE

ERRATIC CREATURE PLAY OBJECT (MORTALLY WOUNDED)

COMMONLY OBSERVED OBJECTS & BEINGS

SLICK-SLAP FOOTBLADES

SLICK-SLAP SLAPPER

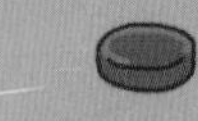

SLICK-SLAP SLAPPEE

FOOT-ORB

FEET FRICTION

FOOT-ORB SUPERVISOR

RECREATIONAL FACE-STRIKING HANDCOVER

SHOVE-TIME ARBITER

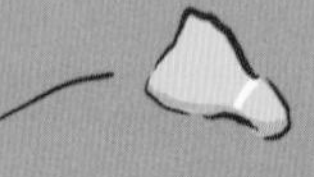

INFRACTION CLOTH

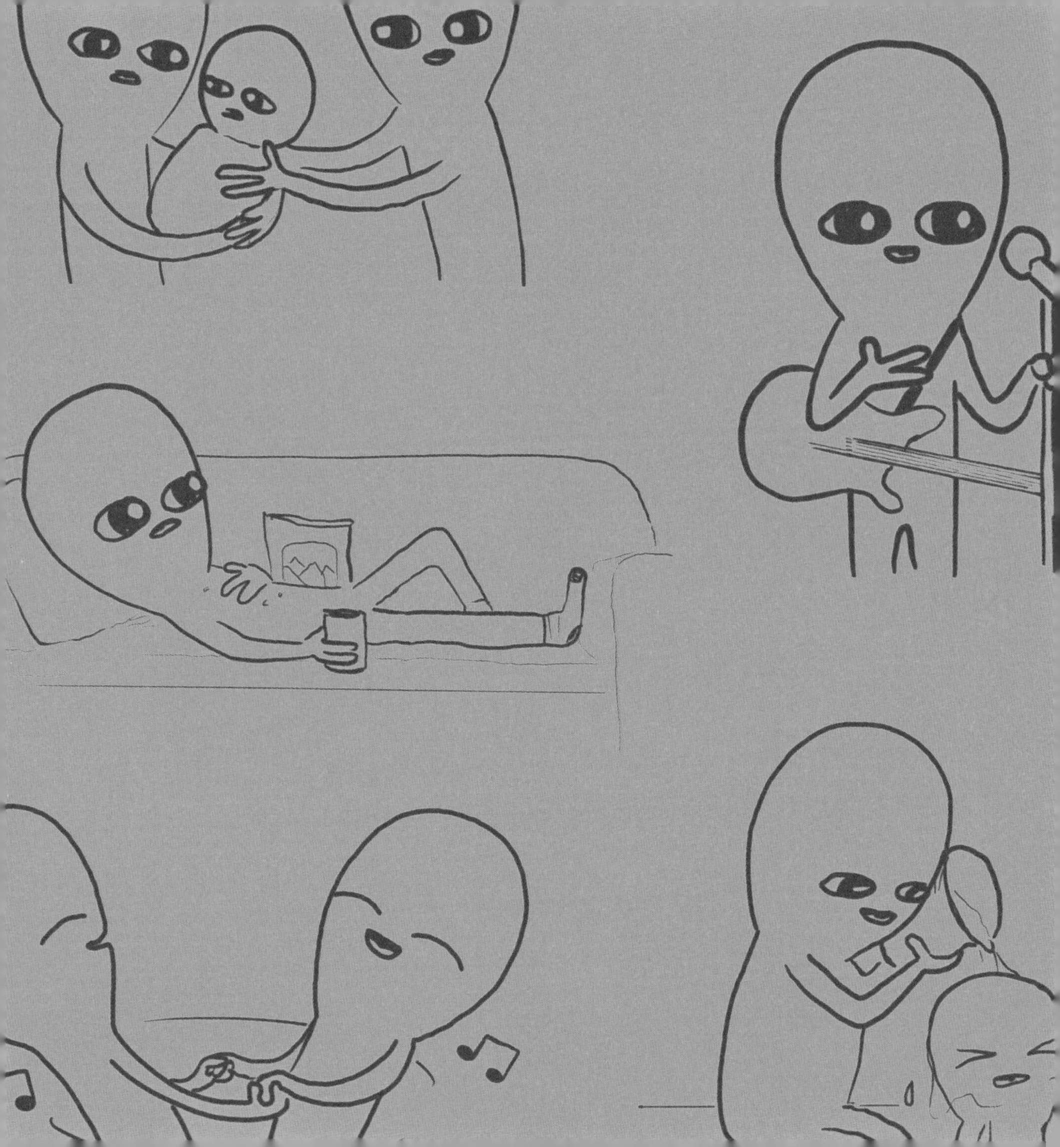

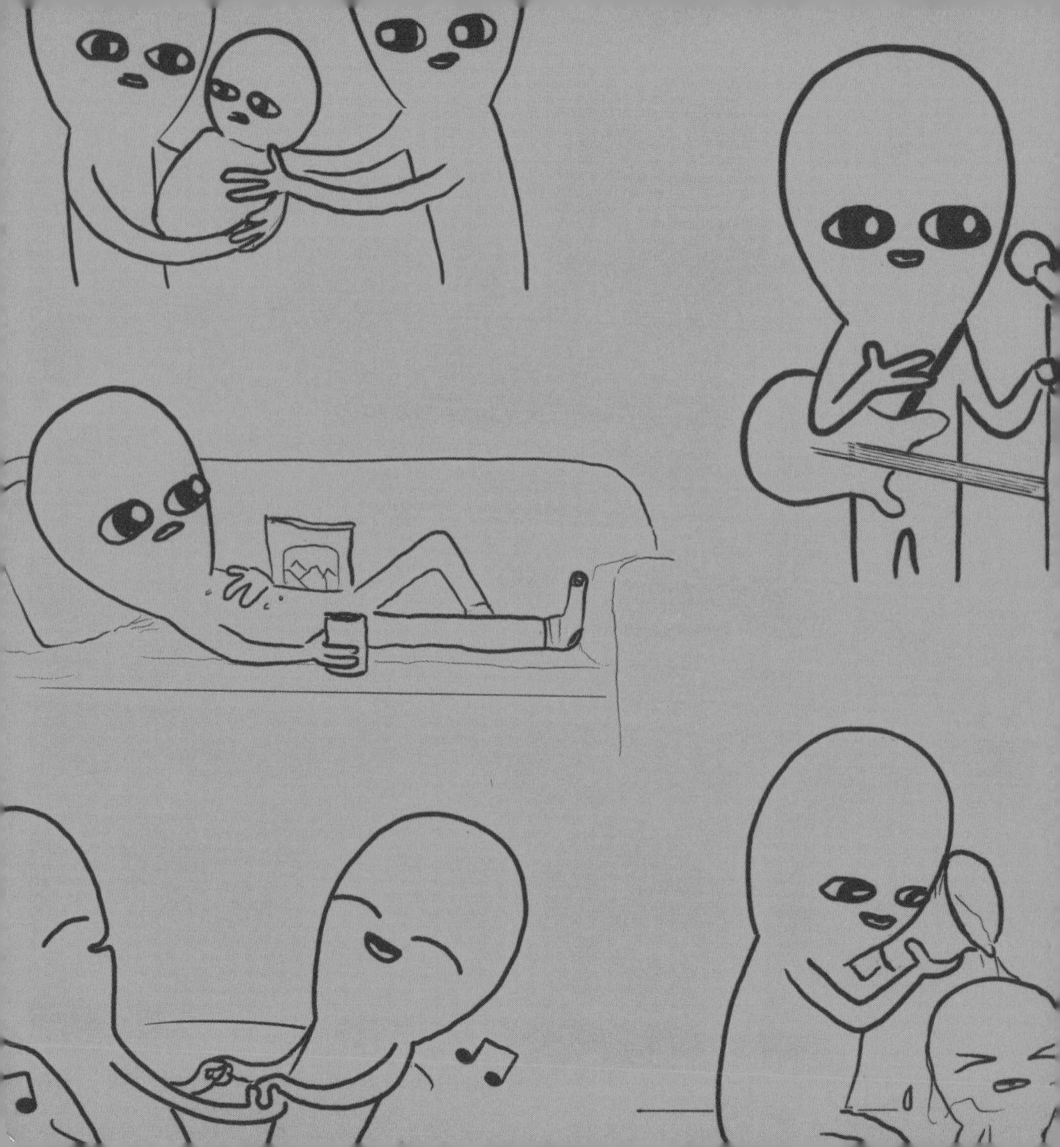